EFFECTIVE
METAPHORS FOR
CHILDREN

A Resource for Therapists,
Parents and Teachers

-by-

Allegra Etheridge

First published 2017, Second imprint 2018
Third imprint 2021

Enquiries should be addressed to Allegra Etheridge
allegra@write-film-edit.co.uk

British Library Cataloguing-in-publication data
A catalogue entry for this book is available from the British Library

ISBN 978-1-911357-41-4

Published by: Write Film Edit, Gloucestershire

Printed and bound by: Seacourt, Pony Road, Horspath Rd, Oxford OX4 2SE

ALLEGRA ETHERIDGE

Allegra is a writer, workplace mediator and coach. She studied Psychology and English at Keele University and has postgraduate qualifications in Publishing, Coaching and Human Resources. She is married to Peter and they live in Gloucestershire.

www.allegrastonemediation.co.uk

TAYMA WALLBRIDGE

Tayma has eight years clinical experience as a solution focused hypnotherapist. She studied Psychology and Sociology at Keele University. She is married to David, has three children and lives in the Lake District.

Their first book '*Effective Metaphors for Hypnotherapy*' was published in 2015. This is their second collaboration.

June, 2021

CONTENTS

INTRODUCTION

It has been an incredibly rewarding time since the publication of our first book, *'Effective Metaphors for Hypnotherapy,'* in March 2015. We have been delighted with the response from practitioners and are also proud to have published a book which has been of positive influence in the therapeutic setting.

Quite early on, our readers told us that there were relatively few effective metaphors available to support children. Children have a unique set of challenges, stresses and opportunities in the modern world and we aim to support them with this book. We know, from first-hand experience, what a huge difference is made to a child's life, if there is somebody there to help them through times of emotional difficulty.

We have focused on areas such as: change, self-acceptance, control of bladder and bowels, confidence, illness, developing resilience, abuse (neglect, physical, sexual and emotional), anger management, fear of authority, developing independence, home environments, making friends, overcoming bullying and addiction to computer games.

Each child will bring a different set of beliefs about themselves and their world and so we have provided a collection of metaphors for you to choose the ones that you believe will resonate most effectively with them.

HOW TO USE THIS BOOK

These metaphors will help you support children and empower them in a gentle, non-directive way to bring about change. These stories are intended to be read by:

- therapists as part of a therapeutic intervention - particularly hypnotherapists
- a teacher as a story to be read and discussed at school
- a parent or guardian, for example as a bedtime story

You could choose to offer the metaphor as a story, an observation about someone you heard about, or a situation you would like them to imagine. This is a matter of choice.

Depending on the situation, you may also wish to read a story to a group of children and ask what the metaphor means e.g. to get them to communicate to each other about the topic of bullying to open up a discussion.

Some readers will have the ability to read a story aloud and effortlessly change the gender as they go. However, not all of us are able to do this, particularly perhaps people who have dyslexia for example. We have therefore duplicated some of the stories by gender to make the book open to all. Our rationale is that if the story can speak to the child in the strongest way possible, then this increases the likelihood of positive change.

Furthermore, we are also aware that many more stories in children's literature have a male rather than a female protagonist and so we wanted to ensure that we have gender-balance in our work. You will therefore notice that this has led to repetition of a proportion of the stories.

Many of the stories sentences deliberately begin with the word 'And' or 'But,' which we appreciate is not grammatically correct. However, because the stories are intended to be read aloud, we have deliberately written them in this way to be more like natural speech.

We have ordered the metaphors alphabetically but you can also cross reference them according to therapeutic goals. You will see that we feel that some stories are able to address several topics simultaneously.

We suggest that you read the stories in advance of your time with the child to ensure that it is appropriate for their age. Some of our stories are geared towards younger children and others to older children. We have not provided a suggested age range because we know how individual a child's maturity and vocabulary can be. However, we suggest that the stories are generally, but not always, appropriate for children up to the age of fourteen. Therapists therefore may also find that some of the stories can be used for adults.

THEORY

Our books are based on the theory constructed by Dr Milton Erickson, the founder of modern hypnotherapy. Erickson's 'solution focused' approach achieved huge success in helping children change their feelings and behaviours. He understood that each of his patients, including children, knew what they were seeking. He also knew that they had the power to change, but that they needed help to overcome natural resistance to change.

Children automatically link up stories (or metaphors) and literal happenings, so that when they hear them, their minds quickly understand what is meant.

If a child listens to a story, the areas within their brains which are responsible for emotions are also activated. For this reason, children will be more fully engaged with a story than a presentation of factual information. Children tend to remember stories for far longer than facts, because they can tend to hold more meaning for them. When stories are told with the intention of changing the way a child thinks, or does things, then the story becomes a therapeutic metaphor. Whether you are a hypnotherapist, or another type of therapist, parent or a teacher who uses metaphors, these stories can be used to maximise a child's potential for change. A good metaphor will symbolically represent the child's problem and offer a solution in an indirect manner. Because it is indirect, the child has to become actively involved in the process of making sense of it and deciding what parts of the metaphor relates to them. If the story is engaging, it will bypass conscious resistance and sink delightfully into the unconscious mind, where it will be thought about for some time. Even if the child does not understand the metaphor, or thinks it's not relevant, their unconscious mind will keep going over it, until some connections are found with their own situation.

The message within the metaphor builds a sense of expectancy in the child that their problem can be solved. And it can stimulate a change in the way they think about their situation. Instead of the solution being presented as advice from a trusted adult, it is discovered by them and so becomes their idea, which is more likely to lead to successful, positive change.

We welcome your feedback on your experience of using this book and wish you every success with your interactions with the children for whom you care.

THERAPEUTIC GOALS

Confidence/Self-belief

Control of Bladder and Bowels

Coping with Illness

Developing Resilience

THE
METAPHORS

ALIEN TEACHERS
(for boys)

I wonder if you can imagine a time, way, way in the future, when the world has changed. For example, humans have learned how to travel at the speed of light. And families even go on holiday to the moon!

And imagine a boy, just like you, as he prepares to go to school. Because, even in the future, children still have to learn and go to school, just as they do now.

The trouble is, the boy just hasn't got used to the alien teachers there. He's a human boy with hands, feet and eyes. But the teachers are from planets at the far end of the universe and they are unfamiliar and strange to him.

The teachers are tall, with green skin and eyes in the back of their head and they make strange sounds when they speak in their own language to each other. The boy hasn't spent much time with aliens - let alone alien teachers. And, if he's honest, they scare him.

But there's something strange about time, which, even though the boy lives in the future, is just the same as it is now. And this is that the more time you spend somewhere - even if it may seem odd at first - it gets more and more normal, until you don't even notice that it is strange any more. And that goes for people too...

And, even though the boy is human and has blood pumping through his body, eyes on the front of his face and a nose and mouth - and the aliens have green skin, eyes on the back of their head and make funny noises, to the boy, they became, somehow, rather normal.

Therapeutic goals:
- Accepting change
- Fear of authority figures

ALIEN TEACHERS
(for girls)

I wonder if you can imagine a time, way, way in the future, when the world has changed. For example, humans have learned how to travel at the speed of light. And families even go on holiday to the moon!

And imagine a girl, just like you, as she prepares to go to school. Because, even in the future, children still have to learn and go to school, just as they do now.

The trouble is, the girl just hasn't got used to the alien teachers there. She's a human girl with hands, feet and eyes. But the teachers are from planets at the far end of the universe and they are unfamiliar and strange to her.

The teachers are tall, with green skin and eyes in the back of their head and they make strange sounds when they speak in their own language to each other. The girl hasn't spent much time with aliens - let alone alien teachers. And, if she's honest, they scare her.

But there's something strange about time, which, even though the girl lives in the future, is just the same as it is now. And this is that the more time you spend somewhere - even though it may seem odd at first - it gets more and more normal, until you don't even notice that it is strange any more. And that goes for people too…

And, even though the girl is human and has blood pumping through her body, eyes on the front of her face and a nose and mouth - and the aliens have green skin, eyes on the back of their head and make funny noises, to the girl, they became, somehow, rather normal.

Therapeutic goals:
- Accepting change
- Fear of authority figures

ANGRY STONES
(for boys)

All over the world children are very different - some are serious, some are cheeky and some like to read and some like to play. Our story is about a boy who was sometimes angry. He would shout and throw things and say bad things that he didn't really mean. People were often hurt by what he said and did when he was angry. And it was not nice to be around such an angry boy.

His father had been angry when he was young but he did not have a temper now and so he decided to help his son. The next time the boy was angry, his father told him: '*Go to the end of the garden and throw a stone into the pond. Then keep throwing stones in there until you stop feeling angry. And the next time you feel like that, go to the end of the garden and do it again.*'

And because the boy was often angry, soon after he stomped up to the end of the garden and threw a stone into the pond. And instead of shouting, throwing things and saying bad things, he did that instead. Sometimes, he threw in many stones.

This went on for some time, until his father felt the moment was right. Then they went up to the end of the garden together. And his father said: '*Take every stone out of the pond.*'

And the boy did what his father told him. He put his hand in the water and felt his stones just below the surface. Where there should have been fish, frogs and water, there was nothing but a thin layer of water over the stones. It took a long time to clear the pond of all the stones. And at the bottom, when he finished, was a puddle of water. Nothing was alive. The boy was surprised and sad.

His father said to him: '*Every stone is an angry word and action you would have made. They would have hurt people in just the same way as you have hurt this pond.*'

And the boy looked at the pile of stones and remembered all the journeys he'd made to the end of the garden. He wondered why, because he'd forgotten all those things that had made him angry.

'*Now fill the pond with water,*' said his father, '*and life will return.*'

And the boy filled the pond to the brim with water from a long hose. And, sure enough, in time, the frogs and fish returned. From time to time, the boy still got angry but when he got to the pond, he saw the precious life there and no longer wanted to throw a stone in. Somehow his anger just melted away.

Therapeutic goals:

- Emotional control/anger management

ANGRY STONES
(for girls)

All over the world children are very different - some are serious, some are cheeky and some like to read and some like to play. Our story is about a girl who was sometimes angry. She would shout and throw things and say bad things that she didn't really mean. People were often hurt by what she said and did when she was angry. And it was not nice to be around such an angry girl.

Her mother had been angry when she was young but she did not have a temper now and so she decided to help her daughter. The next time the girl was angry, her mother told her: *'Go to the end of the garden and throw a stone into the pond. Then keep throwing stones in there until you stop feeling angry. And the next time you feel like that, go to the end of the garden and do it again.'*

And because the girl was often angry, soon after she stomped up to the end of the garden and threw a stone into the pond. And instead of shouting, throwing things and saying bad things, she did that instead. Sometimes, she threw in many stones.

This went on for some time, until her mother felt the moment was right. Then they went up to the end of the garden together. And her mother said: '*Take every stone out of the pond.*'

And the girl did what her mother told her. She put her hand in the water and felt her stones just below the surface. Where there should have been fish, frogs and water, there was nothing but a thin layer of water over the stones. It took a long time to clear the pond of all the stones. And at the bottom, when she finished, was a puddle of water. Nothing was alive. The girl was surprised and sad.

Her mother said to her: '*Every stone is an angry word and action you would have made. They would have hurt people in just the same way as you have hurt this pond.*'

And the girl looked at the pile of stones and remembered all the journeys she'd made to the end of the garden. She wondered why, because she'd forgotten all those things that had made her angry.

'*Now fill the pond with water,*' said her mother, '*and life will return.*'

And the girl filled the pond to the brim with water from a long hose. And, sure enough, in time, the frogs and fish returned. From time to time, the girl still got angry but when she got to the pond, she saw the precious life there and no longer wanted to throw a stone in. Somehow her anger just melted away.

Therapeutic goals:
- Emotional control/anger management

ANXIOUS DAISY

Daisies are cheerful flowers. They have a circular face with a bright gold centre and thin, white petals. Daisies love the sun and they often like to grow in thick, green, grassy lawns.

But one particular daisy never felt quite as cheerful as the others. She worried about herself instead. All day she would ask herself questions like: *'How many of the other daisies are my friend?'* *'What can I do to make more plants my friend?'* *'What do the other plants think of me?'* She was an anxious daisy and, to be honest, she thought a lot about herself.

Near the lawn where the daisy grew, was a stinging nettle, who was hidden in the bushes. You may not know this, but stinging nettles are a bit rude sometimes. And they sting with their leaves - and with what they say. The nettle could hear the daisy talking to herself and became cross. Suddenly, the nettle said to the daisy: *'We plants don't think as much about you - as you think we do!'*

And the daisy became quiet. She couldn't see the nettle. Because the nettle was old and wise and tough, she respected what the nettle said. And the daisy looked around her at the other plants. This time, she took a good look at them.

And, do you know, they were not looking at her. In fact, not one was looking at her at all! What the nettle had said was true, each plant was the centre of their own lives, just as the daisy was of hers.

After that, of course, the daisy did think about herself sometimes, as all daisies do, but she knew that she did not need to really worry about what people thought of her after all.

Therapeutic goals:
- Accepting yourself for who you are
- Confidence/self-belief
- Making friends/developing social skills

BALLOON HAT
(for boys)

You may know that sometimes at a party there is music and sometimes dancing and there are often games and there is nice food to eat. And maybe you can imagine a special party with lots of children being entertained by a Magician?

Well, at this party, the Magician was able to make things appear and disappear again. He could also play tricks with a pack of cards. But, best of all, he could make balloons into dogs and even hats. The children were amazed by him and they asked him to make many different balloon toys, one each.

The children were all having a lot of fun except for one boy who was quieter than the others because he was sad. He was sad because at night, when he was asleep, he wet his bed. He so wanted to be grown up and not wet his bed, but he just didn't know how not to.

The Magician went over to him and asked him: '*What kind of balloon would you like?*'

And the boy quietly said: '*A balloon hat please.*'

'*Very well!*' said the Magician and he blew up balloons and twisted them into different shapes as only a Magician can. And the boy watched closely because it was so wonderful to see his balloon hat being made.

When he had almost finished, the Magician held out the hat to the boy and said: '*You see this last balloon?*'

The boy nodded.

The Magician continued: '*Look how I can release the air from it.*' And he let go of the end very slightly and a small amount of air whistled out. Then he held the end tight again and the balloon stopped whistling. And he did this again and let go of the end very slightly and a small amount of air whistled out. Then he held the end tight again and the balloon stopped whistling.

The Magician then tied a knot in the balloon and twisted it into the hat, which finished it. And the Magician handed the boy the balloon hat.

And the boy realised that he had the power to control his body in the same way that the Magician controlled the air that came out of the balloon.

And even though it looked just the same as all the other balloon hats, the boy felt quite different as soon as he put it on.

After the party, the boy's mother took him home. She looked at him and said: '*My goodness, what a great hat!*' And she looked into his eyes and said: '*You look different, really quite grown up!*'

And the boy smiled because he knew that, in his way, the Magician had worked real magic that day.

Therapeutic goals:

- Control of bladder and bowels

BALLOON HAT

(for girls)

You may know that sometimes at a party there is music and sometimes dancing and there are often games and there is nice food to eat. And maybe you can imagine a special party with lots of children being entertained by a Magician?

Well, at this party, the Magician was able to make things appear and disappear again. He could also play tricks with a pack of cards. But, best of all, he could make balloons into dogs and even hats. The children were amazed by him and they asked him to make many different balloon toys, one each.

The children were all having a lot of fun except for one girl who was quieter than the others because she was sad. She was sad because at night, when she was asleep, she wet her bed. She so wanted to be grown up and not wet her bed, but she just didn't know how not to.

The Magician went over to her and asked her: '*What kind of balloon would you like?*'

And the girl quietly said: '*A balloon hat please.*'

'*Very well!*' said the Magician and he blew up balloons and twisted them into different shapes as only a Magician can. And the girl watched closely because it was so wonderful to see her balloon hat being made.

When he had almost finished, the Magician held out the hat to the girl and said: '*You see this last balloon?*'

The girl nodded.

The Magician continued: '*Look how I can release the air from it.*' And he let go of the end very slightly and a small amount of air whistled out. Then he held the end tight again and the balloon stopped whistling. And he did this again and let go of the end very slightly and a small amount of air whistled out. Then he held the end tight again and the balloon stopped whistling.

The Magician then tied a knot in the balloon and twisted it into the hat, which finished it. And the Magician handed the girl the balloon hat.

And the girl realised that she had the power to control her body in the same way that the Magician controlled the air that came out of the balloon.

And even though it looked just the same as all the other balloon hats, the girl felt quite different as soon as she put it on.

After the party, the girl's father took her home. He looked at her and said: '*My goodness, what a great hat!*' And he looked into her eyes and said: '*You look different, really quite grown up!*'

And the girl smiled because she knew that, in his way, the Magician had worked real magic that day.

Therapeutic goals:
- Control of bladder and bowels

BLOWING BUBBLES

Everyone loves blowing bubbles. We all know how to dip a ring into liquid and blow them into life. Bubbles can be large, small, perfect circles or even long and thin. If you look at bubbles in the sunlight, you can see a rainbow of colours in them. Each is beautiful and unique and special. Bubbles love to float in the air, feeling the gentle current and moving and dancing wherever the breeze takes them.

But bubbles do not last - and all must pop. Some pop very quickly - whilst others are lucky enough to enjoy floating and dancing in the air for longer.

The pattern is always the same for each one. The thing that really matters is the time the bubble lives, floats and dances in that gentle breeze.

Therapeutic goals:
- Bereavement and death

BRIGHT STAR
(for boys)

As you probably know, life can be both good and bad. Just as there is lightness, there is darkness. Just as there is fun, there is also sadness. And although most lives are warm, bright and sunny, sometimes they can also be cold and dark. And you also may have noticed that most people like talking about things that are warm, bright and sunny. This can make it difficult to talk about things that are dark.

And so it was with a boy. His heart was breaking because he had a sad secret. But every time he wanted to tell his secret, he knew that it was from a dark time and he worried and stopped himself. He thought that maybe stories like his would cause a fuss and he felt ashamed. But most of all, he didn't want to be bad. As he kept his secret, his heart broke a little more. Until, one day, he knew he couldn't keep it to himself any longer.

And, as there always is, there was one person he could trust who he decided to see. This lady was kind and wise. And she could see how the boy was struggling to tell her his secret, so she said: '*We are all born good like a bright star. We keep that goodness within us, always, even if we may feel cold sometimes.'*

And the boy told her what was making his heart break. And she did not think he was a bad person, or that he was causing a fuss. And he did not feel ashamed. In fact she was happy that his heart was not breaking any more and that she was able to help.

Later, when the boy became a man and thought back to this, he remembered the good bright star he had always been - and still was.

Therapeutic goals:
- Confidence/self-belief
- Emotional, physical and sexual abuse
- Neglect
- Overcoming bullying

BRIGHT STAR
(for girls)

As you probably know, life can be both good and bad.
Just as there is lightness, there is darkness. Just as there
is fun, there is also sadness. And although most lives are
warm, bright and sunny, sometimes they can also be
cold and dark. And you may have also noticed that most
people like talking about things that are warm, bright
and sunny. This can make it difficult to talk about things
that are dark.

And so it was with a girl. Her heart was breaking
because she had a sad secret. But every time she wanted
to tell her secret, she knew that it was from a dark time
and she worried and stopped herself. She thought that
maybe stories like hers would cause a fuss and she felt
ashamed. But most of all, she didn't want to be bad. As
she kept her secret, her heart broke a little more. Until,
one day, she knew she couldn't keep it to herself any
longer.

And, as there always is, there was one person she could
trust who she decided to see. This lady was kind and
wise. And she could see how the girl was struggling to
tell her the secret, so she said: '*We are all born good like a*

bright star. We keep that goodness within us, always, even if we may feel cold sometimes.'

And the girl told her what was making her heart break. And she did not think she was a bad person, or that she was causing a fuss and she did not feel ashamed. In fact, she was happy that her heart was not breaking any more and that she was able to help.

Later, when the girl became a lady and thought back to this, she remembered the good bright star she had always been - and still was.

Therapeutic goals:
- Confidence/self-belief
- Emotional, physical and sexual abuse
- Neglect
- Overcoming bullying

CLOUD GAZING

I wonder if you can think of a time when you have simply laid back on the grass and just stared up into the sky…

Sometimes the weather is so fine and the sun is so warm that there just doesn't seem anything more relaxing and perfect to do.

And although it's nice to lie with your eyes closed, it's also fun to stare up and watch the clouds.

And you will see that they never stay still. They will put themselves into patterns that look like faces or animals or even mermaids. But they don't ever stay still, because clouds are always changing shape.

Sometimes the cloud shapes are fun and happy and sometimes they are scary or sad - but all pass on. As old clouds move away new, different clouds will appear.

And so it is with life, sometimes quickly and sometimes slowly, change happens. And the wonderful thing about that is that difficult times will pass, just as the clouds change, every moment of every day.

Therapeutic goals:
- Accepting change
- Bereavement and death
- Coping with illness
- Developing resilience
- Moving house

DRAGONFLIES

I wonder if you can think of a glorious summer day. Maybe you have smelt cut grass, heard birds sing or felt the sun on your face? Well, there are places in the world now where the sky is blue, nature is green and lush and it is summer. And, here, amongst the trees and water, you will find dragonflies.

These insects love to fly and they love ponds. They have beautiful turquoise, red, black and yellow bodies which glimmer in the sunlight. They have large eyes that can look in many directions at once. And they fly using their shimmering, red-tipped, transparent wings.

But the most special thing about a dragonfly, is that their life is very short, just a few days or weeks at most. Some people feel very sad for the dragonfly because that does not seem a very long time to them. But other people say it's not the length of your life that matters but what you do in it that counts.

If you were to ask the dragonfly, they would say that they were blessed with a life which had sunshine, water, the smell of cut grass, and the sound of birds. They also know that they are beautiful and they have the amazing ability to fly and see everything with their large eyes. And, to a dragonfly, that is a very wonderful life indeed.

Therapeutic goals:
- Bereavement and death

FAMILY PAINTING
(for boys)

I wonder if you've ever dipped a brush in bright-coloured paint and brought a white sheet of paper to life with a splash of colour. Well, there was once a boy who loved to do this. He would paint many, many pictures. There were lots of things to do at school of course but he liked this the best.

One week, everyone in his class was asked to paint a picture of their family. And so the boy took his brush and painted his family. Later, when the paintings were dry, all the children sat cross-legged in front of the teacher as she showed each painting to the class. The boy's painting was the first to be held up. *'And who is in your family?'* The teacher asked the boy.

And the boy said: *'My Mummy, her boyfriend, my daddy and his girlfriend and all my brothers and sisters.'*

And one of the girls, who was rude and not very kind said: *'Why do you have four parents? That's stupid.'* And the boy felt sad.

The teacher said: *'We all come from different families, some children have more than one Mummy and some have more than one Daddy.'* The teacher held up another painting. *'And who is in your family?'* The teacher asked a girl.

'That's me and my Mum,' she said.

And the boy thought it was a lovely painting.

'But you don't have a Daddy. That's stupid,' said the rude girl, who was not very kind.

And the boy felt sad.

But the teacher said: *'We all come from different families, some people don't have a Daddy.'* Then she held up another painting. *'And who is in this family?'* she asked.

And one of the children said: *'This is me with my two Daddies.'*

And the boy thought the painting was lovely.

And the teacher brought the rude girl, who was not very kind, to stand at the front of the class and said: *'Look at all the wonderful children here. They may be different from each other, but that's what makes the world a wonderful place.'*

And the boy smiled. And he knew that the next time he painted, he would paint all the children in his class with a big smile, just like the one he had right at that moment.

Therapeutic goals:

- Accepting yourself for who you are
- Multi-home families

FAMILY PAINTING
(for girls)

I wonder if you've ever dipped a brush in bright-coloured paint and brought a white sheet of paper to life with a splash of colour. Well, there was once a girl who loved to do this. She would paint many, many pictures. There were lots of things to do at school of course but she liked this the best.

One week, everyone in her class was asked to paint a picture of their family. And so the girl took her brush and painted her family. Later, when the paintings were dry, all the children sat cross-legged in front of the teacher as she showed each painting to the class. The girl's painting was the first to be held up. *'And who is in your family?'* The teacher asked the girl.

And the girl said: *'My Mummy, her boyfriend, my daddy and his girlfriend and all my brothers and sisters.'*

And one of the boys, who was rude and not very kind, said: *'Why do you have four parents? That's stupid.'*

And the girl felt sad.

The teacher said: *'We all come from different families, some children have more than one Mummy and some have more than one Daddy.'* The teacher held up another painting. *'And who is in your family?'* The teacher asked a boy.

'That's me and my Mum,' he said.

And the girl thought it was a lovely painting.

'But you don't have a Daddy. That's stupid,' said the rude boy, who was not very kind.

And the girl felt sad.

But the teacher said: *'We all come from different families, some people don't have a Daddy.'* Then she held up another painting. *'And who is in this family?'* she asked.

And one of the children said: *'This is me with my two Mummies.'*

And the girl thought the painting was lovely.

And the teacher brought the rude boy, who was not very kind, to the front of the class and said to him: *'Look at all the beautiful children here. They may be different from each other, but that's what makes the world a wonderful place.'*

And the girl smiled. And she knew that the next time she painted, she would paint all the children in her class with a big smile, just like the one she had right at that moment.

Therapeutic goals:

- Accepting yourself for who you are
- Multi-home families

FIREWORKS

Over the seas from here, there are many clever people who make fireworks. They are created for us so that we can see amazing displays of beautiful colours, big explosions and circling or shooting rockets spraying coloured lights.

You would think that all rockets would love to play their part but this is not always the case. One Rocket in particular was afraid to be lit because it was shy. It lay worrying next to all the other fireworks in their box as they travelled in a boat across the world to where you live, swaying with the motion of the water.

All the other rockets were asleep and so they didn't hear the shy Rocket. It was talking quietly to itself: *'What happens if people are disappointed with the noise I make? What happens if I don't have a big enough display? What happens if I am not in time? I'm so shy, this could happen...'*

And one of the Sparklers, who never sleep, answered the shy Rocket.

'Rocket, listen, we were all made to light up the night sky.'

The Rocket quietly replied: *'But I'm shy!'*

'Well,' said the Sparkler, *'some fireworks are shy but it's their destiny to light up the night and so that's what we will do.'*

And, for the first time, the Rocket realised that doing what you were meant to do was actually more important than being shy. And it felt relaxed enough to sleep because it knew that when it woke, it was ready to do its job. And as it fell asleep, the Sparklers talked about how much they were looking forward to bonfire night.

Therapeutic goals:

- Accepting yourself for who you are
- Confidence/self-belief

FOOL'S GOLD

Back in time, during one moment in history, a rumour spread that there was a place where you could find gold. It was so exciting for people, whose lives were not as good as they wished them to be. *'Just think of the gold!'* They said to each other.

And thousands of people travelled to this place, determined to find it. They lived in a city of tents, but they left it as much as possible, to look for gold. Many would get up at dawn and go to bed late at night - only frustrated that the dark night and sleep stopped them. It was not as easy as the rumours had said, for there was no gold upon the earth in that place. It was hot work in the sun combing the area looking for it. But they continued on day after day, full of drive and focus.

Once every scrap of land had been searched, the people began looking for gold in rivers. They used round metal pans with a sieve to see if they could separate the gold from the dirt of the river. It was not as easy as the rumours had said for there was no gold in the rivers. It was still hot and now the people were also wet through. But they continued on, day after day, full of drive and focus.

Once the rivers had been thoroughly searched, people began looking for gold by digging underground. They used dynamite to make large holes in the ground and took axes underground. It was not as easy as the rumours had said. And now not only was it hot and wet, but it was also dangerous.

Then - one day - a gold digger found something glittering underground. With delight and amazement, it was brought to the surface. And a person who was a specialist in metals came to study it. And everyone buzzed with excitement. And the specialist looked with a very large magnifying glass for some time at the object. And thousands of people held their breath.

And the specialist said: *'I am sorry but this is 'fool's gold', it looks very much like the real thing but I'm afraid it's worthless.'*

The crowd cried out in dismay and disbelief. How could this be? After searching the earth and the rivers and underground, after all the excitement and effort and time. It was so disappointing!

And the specialist said: '*You cannot have the time back that you have spent looking for 'fool's gold.' It's gone forever. But you have a gift left, if you are willing to take it. Walk away with all the time you have left in your life and use it more wisely.*'

And everyone left that place to seek a better life.

The lump of fool's gold was put in a box and left in the centre of the town next to a ticking clock to remind anyone else who was tempted to dig again.

Therapeutic goals:
- Overcoming addiction to computer games

FOOTBALL BOOTS
(for boys)

There was once a bright green grassy football pitch.
And when all was quiet and the families and children
had gone home, two brothers would put on their boots
from the rack and run to the pitch and play. Because
they were talented, they had learnt many clever moves.
Some said that when they were older, they would make
the national team.

But because life isn't fair and can be a sad and hard
place, I'm sorry to say that the older of the brothers
became very ill, so ill that he could not play. And no
matter what the doctors tried, he was not able to come
back on the pitch - until one Winter's day, he departed
this life forever.

His brother felt the cold stone of sorrow enter his heart
and he vowed never to play again. Although he went to
school and ate and drank, just as he did before, both
pairs of boots stayed in their rack, dusty and unused.
Christmas came and, this year, there was a white
Christmas. As the boy sat looking out of his window,
snow-flakes began to fall. And the snow eventually
turned to slush and then the Spring came. And because

the boy still went through the motions of his life, but with the cold stone of sorrow in his heart, he still stepped outside. He felt the grass beneath his feet.

And he could hear his brother's voice, just as it was when he was still on the earth. And that voice simply said: *'Keep playing.'*

'But you can't play with me any more,' he replied.

And the voice said again - for the final time: *'Keep playing.'*

The boy's feet began walking to the pitch and he walked to the rack and his hands took down his dusty boots. He tried to put them on - but so much time had passed, that he was now too big for them.

But there, in the next place in the rack, were his brother's boots. So he took them and put them on and found that they fitted perfectly.

And the boy walked onto the pitch. And although he was on his own, and it seemed to everyone else that he was on his own, his brother was with him in every move. And the cold stone in his heart evaporated just like the snow and was gone forever.

Therapeutic goals:
- Bereavement and death
- Developing resilience

FOOTBALL BOOTS
(for girls)

There was once a bright green grassy football pitch.
And when all was quiet and the families and children
had gone home, two sisters would put on their boots
from the rack and run to the pitch and play. Because
they were talented, they had learnt many clever moves.
Some said that when they were older, they would make
the national team.

But because life isn't fair and can be a sad and hard
place, I'm sorry to say that the older of the sisters
became very ill, so ill that she could not play. And no
matter what the doctors tried, she was not able to come
back on the pitch - until one Winter's day, she departed
this life forever.

Her sister felt the cold stone of sorrow enter her heart
and she vowed never to play again. Although she went
to school and ate and drank, just as she did before, both
pairs of boots stayed in their rack, dusty and unused.
Christmas came and, this year, there was a white
Christmas. As the girl sat looking out of her window,
snow-flakes began to fall. And the snow eventually
turned to slush and then the Spring came. And because

the girl still went through the motions of her life, but with the cold stone of sorrow in her heart, she still stepped outside. She felt the grass beneath her feet.

And she could hear her sister's voice, just as it was when she was still on the earth. And that voice simply said: '*Keep playing.*'

'*But you can't play with me any more,*' she replied.

And the voice said again - for the final time: '*Keep playing.*'

The girl's feet began walking to the pitch and she walked to the rack and her hands took down her dusty boots. She tried to put them on - but so much time had passed, that she was now too big for them.

But there, in the next place in the rack, were her sister's boots. So she took them and put them on and found that they fitted perfectly.

And the girl walked onto the pitch. And although she was on her own, and it seemed to everyone else that she was on her own, her sister was with her in every move. And the cold stone in her heart evaporated just like the snow.

Therapeutic goals:
- Bereavement and death
- Developing resilience

GARDEN DEN

There were once a brother and sister, who both loved to talk. They had the same mother but different fathers. And although they lived together most of the time, sometimes the boy had to go away and see his father who lived somewhere else - and his sister did not go with him.

They made a den at the bottom of their garden from branches and dried leaves and it was fun to be there together, especially in the hot, summer months. They would often sit there, head to toe and talk about anything from family, to school, to friends, to food and about anything else that sprang to mind. And one day, they started talking about Love.

'You're lucky,' the boy said to his sister, 'Mum lives with your Dad. That must mean that you are more loved than me.'

'No, you're lucky,' his sister replied, 'instead of two parents you have four. That must mean that you have double the love that I do.'

And her brother replied: 'But I only see my Dad and his wife every other weekend, so I don't get as much love as you.'

And so the conversation continued…

The children did not know it but Love was in the garden den that day. And Love sighed because neither of the children was right. Because Love knew that whether you are away from your family or with them and no matter how many parents you have, there is always an endless supply of Love.

Therapeutic goals:
- Accepting yourself for who you are
- Multi-home families

GRANDFATHER CLOCK

A grandfather clock stands as tall as a person, is made of a big rectangular wooden box and a beautiful clock sits right at the top. Inside the box is a heavy, round weight which moves back and forth to mark time. The grandfather clock chimes the hours and ticks loudly, just so you can hear exactly what the time is. And the grandfather clock does not need electricity, it just needs the weight to move back and forth to power it.

There once was a grandfather clock in the hallway of a house where a family lived. There were also many other clocks in the house. And I'm afraid that these clocks thought rather a lot of themselves.

'If it wasn't for me,' said the alarm clock, *'nobody would get up in the morning because I ring to make sure everyone gets to work and school on time.'*

The grandfather clock, who ticked away in the hall, wished he had an alarm.

'Well, if it wasn't for me', said the clock on the cooker, *'the food would burn because I beep when the food is done to make sure that the family's meals are cooked to perfection.'*

And the grandfather clock, who ticked away in the hall, wished he could help cook food.

'*Well, if wasn't for me,*' said the clock on the boiler, '*there would be no heat in the house because I make sure that the house is warm and there is hot water, so the family can bathe.*'

And the grandfather clock, who ticked away in the hall, wished he could help heat water and keep the house warm. In fact, after listening to the other clocks, he felt rather useless and sad.

And so things went on for a while. Until, one day, in the middle of winter, when the family was cooking dinner, there was a power cut. The clock on the oven stopped and the food stopped cooking. The clock on the boiler stopped and the radiators stopped working. The alarm clock by the bed stopped telling the time. In fact, all of the clocks either went blank - or their batteries slowly started to drain.

'*Don't worry!*' The father said to the family, '*this is an adventure! We'll light a fire in the hearth for heat and warmth. We will heat food over it and the good old grandfather clock will tell the time for us.*'

And the grandfather clock realised that he alone could help the family that night. The feeling of being completely essential to the family was thrilling. If you looked at the grandfather clock's face at that moment, the hour and the minute hand positions showed everyone his smiling face. And he proudly ticked the minutes and chimed the hours.

Therapeutic goals:

- Accepting yourself for who you are
- Confidence/self-belief

GREEN BIKE
(for boys)

One summer, a boy wanted to ride his new, bright green bike but every time he tried - he fell off! He really wasn't very good at riding his bike. And he felt very sorry for himself because there was nothing more that he wanted to do.

His father put stabilisers on to the back wheel to stop the bike from falling over. And the boy got on and found he could ride it! And it was wonderful. He enjoyed it so much, he didn't want to stop.

But he did stop. And that night, he worried that he may not be able to ride without the stabilisers.

Over time, he tried and, without really realising it, because it was such fun, he learned to use the gears. And he learned that he should always wear his helmet. And he learnt how to mend a puncture. And he learnt how to ring his bell. And he learnt how to stop quickly if he needed to. He learnt all there was to know. And his father noticed all the skills he had now got and when the boy was asleep, he went down to the garage and took the stabilisers off.

The next day, after school, the boy rode his bike again, as he did every evening.

His father said to him: '*Well done! You don't need your stabilisers!*'

And the boy looked down and was surprised to see that they weren't there. He laughed and said: '*I didn't even notice!*'

And his father smiled and said: '*Practice makes perfect.*'

Therapeutic goals:

- Confidence/self-belief
- Developing resilience
- Gaining independence

GREEN BIKE
(for girls)

One summer, a girl wanted to ride her new, bright green bike but every time she tried - she fell off! She really wasn't very good at riding her bike. And she felt very sorry for herself because there was nothing more that she wanted to do.

Her mother put stabilisers on to the back wheel to stop the bike from falling over. And the girl got on and found she could ride it! And it was wonderful. She enjoyed it so much, she didn't want to stop.

But she did stop and, that night, she worried that she may not be able to ride without the stabilisers.

Over time, she tried and, without really realising it, because it was such fun, she learned to use the gears. And she learned that she should always wear her helmet. And she learnt how to mend a puncture. And she learnt how to ring her bell. And she learnt how to stop quickly if she needed to. She learnt all there was to know. And her mother noticed all the skills she'd got and when the girl was asleep, she went down to the garage and took the stabilisers off.

The next day, after school, the girl rode her bike again, as she did every evening.

Her mother said to her: '*Well done! You don't need your stabilisers!*'

And the girl looked down and was surprised to see that they weren't there. She laughed and said: '*I didn't even notice!*'

And her mother smiled and said: '*Practice makes perfect.*'

Therapeutic goals:
- Confidence/self-belief
- Developing resilience
- Gaining independence

GUINEA PIG
(for boys)

There was once a boy who had a very bad temper. It was not always obvious what made the boy so cross because sometimes he would get angry over the tiniest things. But, whatever it was, he could throw things, shout, slam doors and say cruel, unkind words.

The boy's family learnt to wait until his temper passed. It was not an easy thing to do but they loved him and they hoped that one day he would stop. Like growing out of a pair of shoes, they hoped that he would grow out of his temper.

The boy knew that his temper upset people but he did not try and change. Which is a shame because life has a way of teaching lessons when you don't try and learn them on your own.

There were many good things about the boy, despite his temper and, one of them, was his love for his pet guinea pig. He adored her slanting, black eyes and silky, brown fur. Every morning, he would clean out her cage and give her food pellets, water and sometimes fruit.

But, this morning, he was angry and instead of closing the cage door and carefully fixing the latch, he slammed it. And he did not notice that the latch came loose and the cage door opened. When the boy came home that night from school, his guinea pig was gone.

He searched everywhere he could think of but there was no sign of her. His heart was broken and he cried. He felt guilty for not putting the latch carefully back on the cage.

And just as cross words cannot be undone, so the guinea pig was gone and her being lost could not be undone.

From that day on, the boy, who still sometimes felt cross, did not throw things, shout, slam doors and say cruel, unkind words.

Instead, he would listen to his anger, reason with it and walk away from it.

And each day the conversations with his anger got easier because his anger realised it could no longer win.

He changed towards others and became much calmer and easier to be around and they believed that he had grown out of his temper like an old pair of shoes.

But the truth was that the boy had promised himself that he would never lose anyone or anything to his anger again.

Therapeutic goals:
- Emotional control/anger management

GUINEA PIG
(for girls)

There was once a girl who had a very bad temper. It was not always obvious what made the girl so cross because sometimes she would get angry over the tiniest things. But, whatever it was, she could throw things, shout, slam doors and say cruel, unkind words.

The girl's family learnt to wait until her temper passed. It was not an easy thing to do but they loved her and they hoped that one day she would stop. Like growing out of a pair of shoes, they hoped that she would grow out of her temper.

The girl knew that her temper upset people but she did not try and change. Which is a shame because life has a way of teaching lessons when you don't try and learn them on your own.

There were many good things about the girl, despite her temper and, one of them, was her love for her pet guinea pig. She adored his slanting, black eyes and silky, brown fur. Every morning, she would clean out his cage and give him food pellets, water and sometimes fruit.

But, this morning, she was angry and instead of closing the cage door and carefully fixing the latch, she slammed it. And she did not notice that the latch came loose and the cage door opened. When the girl came home that night from school, her guinea pig was gone.

She searched everywhere she could think of but there was no sign of him. Her heart was broken and she cried. She felt guilty for not putting the latch carefully back on the cage.

And just as cross words cannot be undone, so the guinea pig was gone and him being lost could not be undone.

From that day on, the girl, who still sometimes felt cross, did not throw things, shout, slam doors and say cruel, unkind words.

Instead, she would listen to her anger, reason with it and walk away from it.

And each day the conversations with her anger got easier because her anger realised it could no longer win.

She changed towards others and became much calmer and easier to be around and they believed that she had grown out of her temper like an old pair of shoes.

But the truth was that the girl had promised herself that she would never lose anyone or anything to her anger again.

Therapeutic goals:
- Emotional control/anger management

HONEY BEES

Now let's just think about honey bees. They are loved because not only do they make delicious honey but they also pollinate flowers. And by doing this, they help make delicious fruit.

But the honey bee has a flaw - its temper. Most people don't know this because they rarely see such helpful, friendly bees get angry. The reason is because they have learnt to manage their tempers.

Honey bees are just like people because there are many, many people who have a temper and just don't show it - because they have learnt not to.

The reason why honey bees don't show their temper is because they always sting afterwards and after they have stung somebody, they use all the energy in their body and they die. And because honey bees love to make honey and to live, they do everything not to get cross and not to sting.

Having a temper can sometimes also hurt people and make them sad. And people know that there are other ways of talking to people or showing how they feel than by stinging with their words.

And so for every honey bee you see, remember that there is also a person who has learnt not to be cross and who had made their life sweet, like honey.

Therapeutic goals:
- Emotional control/anger management
- Making friends/developing social skills

MONKEY SCHOOL
(for boys)

Monkeys are clever. Although they live in the jungle and they are animals - and we are humans - they are very much like us.

And, just like us, they need to be taught things. The older monkeys teach the younger ones how to live in the jungle.

One day, an older monkey showed a younger monkey how to eat a banana. The younger one did not know how to easily find the fruit inside the skin and so the older monkey peeled it carefully to show him how. The younger monkey was delighted to eat the fruit. He had been biting the banana skin - to get to the fruit - and the skin did not taste good!

The following day, I'm sorry to say that the younger monkey forgot how to peel the banana and tried to bite the skin again. The old monkey was annoyed to see it. And monkeys can be scary when they get a bit cross. They also make strange loud noises and, as they are big and strong, they can seem very large to a younger monkey.

As the younger monkey swung, branch to branch, to his favourite tree, where he slept at night, he was sorry about the banana and frightened of the older monkey.

'I don't want to see that bad tempered old monkey again,' he said to himself. *'And I don't want a banana again either. I don't think I want to go back to that part of the jungle again.'*

But, that night, there was a lot of chatter in the trees from the other monkeys before they went to sleep. Some were saying how much they had enjoyed learning to swing through the trees, others said that they were looking forward to learning how to pick nits out of each other's backs. They were laughing because they were looking forward to another day in that part of the jungle.

And the young monkey knew that he would miss out on all the fun parts of being in the jungle if he stayed in his tree. And so, the next morning, he went out with the others.

The old monkey was there but was no longer cross, it was all forgotten. Today, he helped young monkeys to avoid snakes, which is a very useful thing to learn.

And the young monkey realised that the old monkey had been trying to help him and that sometimes being a little cross meant that you remembered important things. Because the younger monkey had remembered how to peel a banana that day and would every day afterwards.

Therapeutic goals:
- Fear of authority figures
- Gaining independence

MONKEY SCHOOL
(for girls)

Monkeys are clever. Although they live in the jungle and they are animals - and we are humans - they are very much like us.

And, just like us, they need to be taught things. The older monkeys teach the younger ones how to live in the jungle.

One day, an older monkey showed a younger monkey how to eat a banana. The younger one did not know how to easily find the fruit inside the skin and so the older monkey peeled it carefully to show her how. The younger monkey was delighted to eat the fruit. She had been biting the banana skin - to get to the fruit - and the skin did not taste good!

The following day, I'm sorry to say that the younger monkey forgot how to peel the banana and tried to bite the skin again. The old monkey was annoyed to see it. And monkeys can be scary when they get a bit cross. They make strange loud noises and, as they are big and strong, they can seem very large to a young monkey.

As the younger monkey swung, branch to branch, to her favourite tree, where she slept at night, she was sorry about the banana and frightened of the older monkey.

'I don't want to see that bad tempered old monkey again,' she said to herself. *'And I don't want a banana again either. I don't think I want to go back to that part of the jungle again.'*

But, that night, there was a lot of chatter in the trees from the other monkeys before they went to sleep. Some were saying how much they had enjoyed learning to swing through the trees, others said that they were looking forward to learning how to pick nits out of each other's backs. They were laughing because they were looking forward to another day in that part of the jungle.

And the young monkey knew that she would miss out on all the fun parts of being in the jungle if she stayed in her tree. And so, the next morning, she went out into the jungle with the others.

The old monkey was there but was no longer cross, it was all forgotten. Today, he helped young monkeys to avoid snakes, which is a very useful thing to learn.

And the young monkey realised that the old monkey had been trying to help her and that sometimes being a little cross meant that you remembered important things. Because the younger monkey had remembered how to peel a banana that day and would every day afterwards.

Therapeutic goals:
- Fear of authority figures
- Gaining independence

MOOD CLOUD

I'm not sure if you know this, only a few people do, but around every person is a coloured mood cloud. This cloud sits around everybody's head and although it is invisible, sometimes you can sense it.

And a mood cloud can be all sorts of different colours.

Sometimes the cloud can be yellow and happy.

Other days, the cloud can be black and angry.

From time to time, the cloud can be red and excited.

And on days when the cloud is blue, the person will be sad.

Sometimes children think that they can't control the colour of the mood cloud.

But the truth is, if you think hard enough, you can change its colour just with the power of your thoughts.

And the cleverest magic is when you turn black or blue clouds to yellow and red clouds just with happy positive thoughts.

Because you own your mood cloud.

Therapeutic goals:
- Emotional control/anger management

OLD JUMPER
(for boys)

Let's imagine a boy who was often hungry and lonely and his clothes were dirty. Today, when he went to school, he wore a very old, dirty jumper.

And his kind teacher noticed this and so she decided to talk to him, when the other children went out to play. She decided to ask some questions to encourage the boy to think.

'Everyone should live in a nice warm house and have enough to eat. Do you?' she asked.

'No, but it's OK,' he replied.

'Everyone should have someone to talk to, who listens to their news and wants them to be happy. Do you?'

'No, but it's OK,' he replied.

'All children should have family who know where they are. Do you?'

'No, but it's OK,' he replied.

'And everyone should have clean clothes to wear. Do you?'

And the boy looked down at his jumper and he saw that there were holes in it and that it was stained and dirty. And, in that moment, he could not ignore the truth.

And so the boy honestly told his kind teacher: *'No, I don't.'*

And his teacher nodded and because she was kind, she promised to help him. She understood that the boy was special, even though he was wearing a dirty jumper.

And, for the first time in a long time, the boy knew that there was someone who really cared about him. He sighed because telling the truth made him feel so relieved.

And he knew that a better life was there, if he wanted it, now he was ready to tell the truth.

Years in the future, when this boy was a man, he kept his old jumper and would look at it and remember the first day of a bright new chapter in his life.

Therapeutic goals:
- Emotional/sexual abuse
- Neglect

OLD JUMPER
(for girls)

Let's imagine a girl who was often hungry and lonely and her clothes were dirty. Today, when she went to school, she wore a very old, dirty jumper.

And her kind teacher noticed this and so she decided to talk to her, when the other children went out to play. She asked some questions to encourage the girl to think.

'Everyone should live in a nice warm house and have enough to eat. Do you?' she asked.

'No, but it's OK,' she replied.

'Everyone should have someone to talk to, who listens to their news and wants them to be happy. Do you?'

'No, but it's OK,' she replied.

'All children should have family who know where they are. Do you?'

'No, but it's OK,' she replied.

'And everyone should have clean clothes to wear. Do you?'

And the girl looked down at her jumper and she saw that there were holes in it and that it was stained and dirty. And, in that moment, she could not ignore the truth.

And so the girl honestly told her kind teacher: *'No I don't.'*

And her teacher nodded and because she was kind she promised to help her - she understood that she was a special girl, even though she was wearing a dirty jumper.

And, for the first time in a long time, the girl knew that there was someone who really cared about her. She sighed because telling the truth made her feel so relieved.

And she knew that a better life was there, if she wanted it, now she was ready to tell the truth.

Years in the future, when this girl was a lady, she kept her old jumper and would look at it and remember the first day of a bright new chapter in her life.

Therapeutic goals:
- Emotional/sexual abuse
- Neglect

OUR VOLCANO

Now, I'm going to tell you about an island a long way away from here. This island is surrounded by a turquoise ocean and the sun beats warmly on it. And, right in the middle of the island, is a large, quiet volcano. It is the biggest volcano anyone knew.

The other volcanoes on nearby islands, I'm sad to say, gush lava and make ash. This burns the land around them and poisons the air. But our volcano is peaceful.

The other volcanoes laugh at our quiet volcano for being so quiet, calling our volcano: '*chicken*' and '*wimp.*'

And although our volcano could have got angry too, like every other volcano there, our volcano decided not to. Our volcano looked at the other islands with their burnt land. And our volcano saw that their trees and birds had gone and that their air was too smoky for any living thing to find a home.

Our volcano knew that it had tonnes of boiling lava inside and our volcano could have made an ash cloud big enough to cover the whole sea. But this was not what our volcano wanted to do. Our volcano's own island had green forests, clear rivers, happy animals, flying birds, chirping insects and fresh air and so our volcano did not say a word.

But on the day the angry volcanoes called out '*chicken!*' and '*wimp!*' for the final time, our volcano actually laughed at them. The laugh made a quake rip across the seas and it rocked every other volcano with its power.

And they realised that just because our volcano was quiet, it did not mean that our volcano was afraid. And the other volcanoes were never rude to our volcano again.

And our volcano lived in paradise, with green forests, clear rivers, happy animals, flying birds, chirping insects and fresh air.

Therapeutic goals:
- Emotional control/anger management
- Overcoming bullying

OYSTER'S PEARL

Oysters are small, hard creatures that live in the sea. They are rough and grey and about the size of a hand. They are perfectly designed for where they live in the cool, salty ocean. Their tough shell can weather any stormy sea. No matter how harsh the waves, an oyster is built to remain whole and strong. Inside, it has a soft centre, which drinks in salt water and finds lots of good things in the water to live off.

But, for a small number of oysters, just like for a small number of children, problems can happen. Oysters sometimes get a large grain of sand inside them which sticks inside their soft centre. It's not what the oyster wants, just like a child, for example, who may not want to get ill. But that's just the way the sea is. And it's the way the human body is. As sad as the oyster is and as sad as the child is, neither have any choice.

But do you know? Life is a wonderful mystery. And sometimes what seems a very bad thing, can turn out to be just the opposite. Because, over time, the grain of sand that's in the soft oyster gets wrapped in lots of layers of beautiful ivory. And the grain gradually turns into a clean, perfectly round pearl. It makes that oyster very rare and very special.

And this is just the same as a child's illness because it makes them grow in an amazing way. Other children do not have that happen to them - which means that every child who has been, or is now ill, is special.

And sometimes, people who really love the child will see the pearl inside them - clean, perfectly round and beautiful.

Therapeutic goals:
- Coping with illness

PICTURE BOOK

Now let's just think of the perfect garden for a moment.
I wonder if you imagine it like a picture in a picture
book.

Maybe it has a tidy, green lawn, one or two straight
leafy trees, a perfectly painted white, wooden fence, a
flower bed with roses - in full bloom of course - and a
pond with a plump frog sitting on a lily pad.

Now let's compare it to a real garden. In real gardens,
the lawn may be full of dandelions or it may need
cutting.

A real garden may have an orchard of trees or just one
tree, which has lost its leaves in winter.

A real garden may have a fence which may need a coat
of paint or there may even be no boundary to the
garden at all.

A real garden may have roses, or there may be many
other different flowers growing there.

And, as for the pond, a real garden may have ten frogs or no frogs at all.

And a perfect garden is lovely but just like the perfect family, it is something that isn't real. Families are all unique though - and if you think about it - being unique can be better than being perfect sometimes.

Therapeutic goals:
- Accepting yourself for who you are
- Multi-home families

PINCH-PUNCH
(for boys)

The phrase 'pinch, punch, the first of the month' was something that one boy heard a lot.

I'm sorry to say that these words were said almost daily - and by people that he knew. Sometimes they were just the words and sometimes the word 'pinch' became a real pinch and sometimes the word 'punch' became a real punch.

And the boy didn't know why it happened to him because the truth is, there is never a good reason for bad words and never a good reason for pinching or punching.

And the boy shrank inside each time he heard and felt this until he felt very small inside indeed.

And people who feel small inside learn to make their voices very quiet too. They can seem timid. This makes some people feel that it is easier to be cruel to them because their voice cannot be heard.

Sometimes kind people he trusted tried to talk to him and help him but because his voice was so small, he couldn't say anything, which made him very sad.

But the amazing, mysterious thing about people is that even if sometimes they don't realise it, there is always a pathway to find exactly what they need. It's just a question of knowing how to find it. And the world can change when they walk down that path.

And the boy wanted to find it because he didn't want this to happen to him any more.

And, one day, it came clear to him. It was simple. He decided that each time it happened, from that moment on, instead of feeling smaller, he would feel bigger instead and his path was powerful.

And as he grew bigger inside, so his small voice got louder and clearer. And each time he grew inside, it became almost impossible for him to be spoken nastily to, or to be pinched or punched.

And, with that clear voice, he found the people he trusted and was able to speak to them. Together, it stopped for good. But what never stopped was his clear voice which stayed with him for the rest of his life.

Therapeutic goals:
- Overcoming bullying
- Physical abuse

PINCH-PUNCH
(for girls)

The phrase 'pinch, punch, the first of the month' was something that one girl heard a lot.

I'm sorry to say that these words were said almost daily - and by people that she knew. Sometimes they were just the words and sometimes the word 'pinch' became a real pinch and sometimes the word 'punch' became a real punch.

And the girl didn't know why it happened to her because the truth is, there is never a good reason for bad words and never a good reason for pinching or punching.

And the girl shrank inside each time she heard and felt this until she felt very small inside indeed.

And people who feel small inside learn to make their voices very quiet too. They can seem timid. This makes some people feel that it is easier to be cruel to them because their voice cannot be heard.

Sometimes kind people she trusted tried to talk to her and help her but because her voice was so small, she couldn't say anything, which made her very sad.

But the amazing, mysterious thing about people is that even if sometimes they don't realise it, there is always a pathway to find exactly what they need. It's just a question of knowing how to find it. And the world can change when they walk down that path.

And the girl wanted to find it because she didn't want this to happen to her any more.

And, one day, it came clear to her. It was simple. She decided that each time it happened, from that moment on, instead of feeling smaller, she would feel bigger instead. And her path was powerful.

And as she grew bigger inside, so her small voice got louder and clearer. And each time she grew inside, it became almost impossible for her to be spoken nastily to, or to be pinched or punched.

And, with that clear voice, she found the people she trusted and was able to speak to them. Together, it stopped for good. But what never stopped was her clear voice which stayed with her for the rest of her life.

Therapeutic goals:

- Overcoming bullying
- Physical abuse

PLAYTIME
(for boys)

All schools have playtime and one boy liked this time of the day the most. He would run with his friends. And they would have many games. The break never seemed long enough.

But, one day, he ran too fast and fell and scraped his knees and hands on the rough tarmac. And it hurt him a lot - but he didn't cry.

The teacher cleaned the wounds and put plasters on his knees. In fact, they were rather special plasters, with pictures of dinosaurs on, which the boy liked very much.

'I will have to stop running when I go and play now,' he said sadly to the teacher.

And the teacher replied: *'Don't give up what you enjoy, just be careful. Keep going - everyone falls down sometimes.'* And the boy thought that he would be very sorry to give up running in his playtime. He thanked the teacher and stopped for a moment and thought - should he run again or should he walk?

And he decided that if he was a little more careful he would run again because even though he may fall again, running was much more fun.

Therapeutic goals:

- Confidence/self-belief
- Developing resilience

PLAYTIME
(for girls)

All schools have playtime and one girl liked this time of the day the most. She would run with her friends. And they would have many games. The break never seemed long enough.

But, one day, she ran too fast and fell and scraped her knees and hands on the rough tarmac. And it hurt her a lot - but she didn't cry.

The teacher cleaned the wounds and put plasters on her knees. In fact, they were rather special plasters, with pictures of cats on, which the girl liked very much.

'I will have to stop running when I go and play now,' she said sadly to the teacher.

And the teacher replied: *'Don't give up what you enjoy, just be careful. Keep going - everyone falls down sometimes.'*

And the girl thought that she would be very sorry to give up running in her playtime. She thanked the teacher and stopped for a moment and thought - should she run again or should she walk?

And she decided that if she was a little more careful she would run again because even though she may fall again, running was much more fun.

Therapeutic goals:
- Confidence/self-belief
- Developing resilience

POST BOX
(for boys)

The boy in this story loved posting letters. His parents wrote many letters. Some addresses were typed, others were hand written, some letters were stamped and some didn't need a stamp at all.

Every time the boy went to the shops he would ask his parents: *'Is there a letter to post?'* And if there was, they would hand it to him and help him post it by picking him up so he could reach into the slot. He knew, with excitement, that each letter was going to travel a long way to find the person it was written to.

One day, his parents gave him a pile of letters but met some friends nearby and began chatting - instead of helping him like they normally did. So, the boy tried to post the letters on his own.

Well, even though he put his arms as straight as he could, he was too small to reach the slot. Part of him wanted to run to and ask his parents to post them for him. But he did not want to give up just because it was difficult.

Next, he stood on tiptoes but still the letters couldn't quite reach the slot. In truth, he was a little wobbly, but he did not want to give up.

Next, he bent his knees and jumped up in the air. He jumped so high that he was able to push the letters into the slot. He had done it on his own! And he realised that there were probably many other things he could do now on his own.

And, do you know, a year later, when he posted a letter that he'd written himself in that same box, it seemed a lot smaller than he remembered. He could really quite easily reach in and he realised how much he had grown up.

Therapeutic goals:
- Developing resilience
- Gaining independence

POST BOX
(for girls)

The girl in this story loved posting letters. Her parents wrote many letters. Some addresses were typed, others were hand written, some letters were stamped and some didn't need a stamp at all.

Every time the girl went to the shops she would ask her parents: *'Is there a letter to post?'* If there was, they would hand it to her and help her post it by picking her up so she could reach into the slot. She knew, with excitement, that each letter was going to travel a long way to find the person it was written to.

One day, her parents gave her a pile of letters but met some friends nearby and began chatting - instead of helping her like they normally did. So, the girl tried to post the letters on her own.

Well, even though she put her arms as straight as she could, she was too small to reach the slot. Part of her wanted to run to and ask her parents to post them for her. But she did not want to give up just because it was difficult.

Next, she stood on tiptoes but still the letters couldn't quite reach the slot. In truth, she was a little wobbly but she did not want to give up.

Next, she bent her knees and jumped up in the air. She jumped so high that she was able to push the letters into the slot. She had done it on her own! And she realised that there were probably many other things she could do now on her own.

And, do you know, a year later, when she posted a letter that she'd written herself in that same box, it seemed a lot smaller than she remembered. She could really quite easily reach in and she realised how much she had grown up.

Therapeutic goals:
- Developing resilience
- Gaining independence

RAINCLOUD

One small cloud had only been in the world a short time and so it was not used to knowing how a cloud should behave. *'When is the right time to rain?'* it wondered, *'and when is the right time to hail?'*

The small cloud never seemed to get it right and it sometimes rained when it shouldn't, like when it was asleep. And the small cloud was ashamed, as the other bigger clouds seemed to only rain and hail when they were awake.

Then, the bright blue sky, where this cloud lived, got cold and the raindrops which made up the small cloud formed into hailstones.

'Right,' thought the little cloud. *'I will try not to hail.'* And it did all it could to keep the hailstones from falling. It was painful and the small cloud was so tight it could not float far from the same spot in the sky. It was such an effort that it could not enjoy the warm sun on his back, like the other clouds did.

And hailstones fell out one day anyway and not when the small cloud wanted them to. And the little cloud felt sad.

The big clouds noticed how the little cloud felt and gathered around it and pushed their soft whiteness against it in comfort.

You may not know this, but clouds are kind because it's their job to moisten the earth so plants and trees can grow. And they said to the small cloud: '*You can control when it rains and you can control when it hails. Just learn to enjoy emptying your refreshing water - and your hailstones - onto the land and onto the sea. It is the most natural thing in the world and it feels good too. We do this every day - and you are just like us.*'

And the big clouds parted and the small cloud floated away and thought about what they'd said.

The next time it felt it needed to rain and hail, the small cloud just knew it. And it rained water onto the land and then it hailed hailstones onto the sea. The feeling of release was exactly as the larger clouds said, it felt good too.

Afterwards, the small cloud floated along with the wind in the bright blue sky and felt the warm sun on its back.

Therapeutic goals:
- Control of bladder and bowels
- Emotional control/anger management

SANDCASTLE

One lovely, warm, Summer's day a family went to the beach. They all decided to build the biggest and most fancy sandcastle and take photos of it when they'd finished.

The spot to make it was found. It was flat and white, but the sand was still wet enough to mould. Building the sandcastle took hours. The family made walls, turrets and even stuck in jolly flags on little wooden pegs. They scooped out a moat and the children decorated the castle with shells. It truly was the biggest and best sandcastle on the beach. The children thought it may have been the biggest and best sandcastle there ever was!

But just before they took their photos, the tide came in and a large wave rolled up the beach and covered the sandcastle. It took down the turrets and flags. It flooded the moat. Some of the shells were washed out to sea. It was a disaster!

The children were so disappointed that the beautiful sandcastle was now just a heap of wet sand that they cried. But their grandfather, who knew everything because he was so old, shrugged his shoulders. '*Things like this happen when you are on the beach.*'

'*I'm never making a sandcastle again!*' One of the children shouted out. '*Yes, what's the point?*' said another.

But their grandfather said: '*Sometimes life doesn't work out the way we want. But remember the pleasure we had in making the sandcastle together? Next time, we will build it further from the shore, away from the waves. And it will be just as good as this one - if not better.*'

'*But it may get washed away again!*' one of the children said.

'*Yes,*' said their grandfather, '*but, if it does, we will just build it again.*'

Therapeutic goals:
- Accepting change
- Developing resilience

SEA HORSE

(for boys)

You may know that there is even more sea than land in this world. And in the deep, blue sea there are many creatures, including fish, which are all different colours, sizes and shapes. I don't know if you know what sea horses look like, but they are also fish, even though they have a face that looks like a horse. They hold onto weed with their tails and they stand upright. One day, a young fish swam in and out of the sea horses. He flicked his tail and they bobbed about in his wake, with their tails tied to the weed. The young fish stopped and stared at one particular sea horse.

The sea horse said nothing.

'*Can't you swim?*' said the young fish, trying to provoke him.

The sea horse said nothing.

'*You look like a horse!*' scoffed the young fish.

The sea horse still said nothing,

'Horses live on land - you shouldn't be in the sea,' said the young fish rudely.

And the sea horse finally replied: *'I am unique but I am also a fish. But the difference between us is that I make the sea a better place and you do not.'*

The young fish laughed at the sea horse as he swam away and pretended that the words meant nothing to him. But, secretly, part of him knew that the sea horse was right and he didn't like himself very much when he thought about it.

And the sea horse continued to bob in the ocean with his tail tucked safely around the long green weed enjoying his life in the dark blue sea and making it a better place.

Therapeutic goals:
- Accepting yourself for who you are
- Making friends/developing social skills
- Overcoming bullying

SEA HORSE
(for girls)

You may know that there is even more sea than land in this world. And in the deep, blue sea there are many creatures, including fish, which are all different colours, sizes and shapes. I don't know if you know what sea horses look like, but they are also fish, even though they have a face that looks like a horse. They hold onto weed with their tails and they stand upright. One day, a young fish swam in and out of the sea horses. She flicked her tail and they bobbed about in her wake, with their tails tied to the weed. The young fish stopped and stared at one particular sea horse.

The sea horse said nothing.

'*Can't you swim?*' said the young fish, trying to provoke her.

The sea horse said nothing.

'*You look like a horse!*' scoffed the young fish.

The sea horse still said nothing.

'Horses live on land - you shouldn't be in the sea,' said the young fish rudely.

The sea horse finally replied: *'I am unique but I am also a fish. But the difference between us is that I make the sea a better place and you do not.'*

The young fish laughed at the sea horse as she swam away and pretended that the words meant nothing to her. But, secretly, part of her knew that the sea horse was right. Secretly, she didn't like herself very much when she thought about it.

And the sea horse continued to bob in the ocean with her tail tucked safely around the long green weed enjoying her life in the dark blue sea and making it a better place.

Therapeutic goals:
- Accepting yourself for who you are
- Making friends/developing social skills
- Overcoming bullying

SHINY BUILDING

The Wind whistled round the big, shiny Building in the heart of the city.

The Wind had been there since the beginning of time and had seen the shiny new building built. In fact, the Wind and had seen the land before people, even when it was walked over by dinosaurs. And because the Wind was so old, it was also very wise as well as still being curious about new things.

The Wind saw the many people go into the office and stare at computer screens day after day and because the Wind was curious it decided to talk to the Building.

The Wind asked: *'Building, have you smelled the sweet scent of cut grass in the summer?'*

And the Building replied: *'No Wind, there is no grass near here and I cannot see or smell it. I can only see grass sometimes in the computer screens that are in me.'*

And the Wind asked: *'Building, have you felt the salty sea against your windows when I stir the water in a storm?'*

And the Building replied: '*No, there is no sea near me and I cannot move to feel it. I can only see the sea sometimes in the computer screens that are in me.*'

And the Wind continued: '*Building, have you heard bees buzzing around flowers in the summer?*'

And the Building replied: '*No Wind, bees do not come near because there are no flowers. I can only see the bees sometimes in the computer screens that are in me.*'

And the Wind said: '*But these pleasures are the most wonderful parts of being alive.*'

And the Building replied: '*Yes, I believe you, but I am not really alive. I am lit up by electricity. If it stopped, I wouldn't exist.*'

And the Wind asked: '*Building, what about the computer screens that are inside you? Are they alive?*'

And the Building replied: '*They look alive but they are not. Only the people are alive.*'

And the Wind finally asked: '*Do the people in the building smell the grass, feel the sea, hear the bees or see the flowers?*'

And the Building replied: '*No, they only think they do, when they look at their computers.*'

And the Wind left the Building and the computer screens which weren't real. And the Wind smelt the grass, felt the sea, heard the bees and saw the flowers and whispered to the people to join it.

Therapeutic goals:

- Overcoming addiction to computer games

SPLASHING PUDDLES
(for boys)

When you think about rain, you may think about the sound it makes as it hits a window pane. Or you may think about the feel of large, wet drops on your head, when you don't have your head covered. Or you may think about the smell of rain in the summer as it evaporates from hot roads. Or may even think about the taste of rain, if you open your mouth and let drops fall in.

And, now, let's imagine a place where a lot of rain has fallen and large, fresh puddles form. On this day, two children put on their boots and run outside to play.

The girl sees them and shouts out in delight: '*Come on! Let's jump and splash in the puddles!*'

But the boy stands back for a moment and says: '*What if I get wet and cold?*'

'*Well,*' his friend cheerily replies, '*you'll get wet and cold!*'

'*What if that dirty water goes over the edge of my boot and into my socks and feet?*' the boy goes on.

'Then you'll get dirty wet feet!' the girl replies.

And she jumps right in to the nearest puddle. Because what's more important at that moment is the sheer enjoyment and excitement of splashing in puddles.

And so that's what they do all morning - laugh and jump and splash.

And do you know? The next day all the puddles have gone! And the boy realises that the opportunity to splash in the puddles has gone too. But he's glad he enjoyed it when he did. For who knows when it will rain so much again?

Therapeutic goals:

- Confidence/self-belief

SPLASHING PUDDLES
(for girls)

When you think about rain, you may think about the sound it makes as it hits a window pane. Or you may think about the feel of large, wet drops on your head, when you don't have your head covered. Or you may think about the smell of rain in the summer as it evaporates from hot roads. Or may even think about the taste of rain, if you open your mouth and let drops fall in.

And, now, let's imagine a place where a lot of rain has fallen and large, fresh puddles form. On this day, two children put on their boots and run outside to play.

The boy sees them and shouts out in delight: '*Come on! Let's jump and splash in the puddles!*'

But the girl stands back for a moment and says: '*What if I get wet and cold?*'

'*Well,*' her friend cheerily replies, '*you'll get wet and cold!*'

'*What if that dirty water goes over the edge of my boot and into my socks and feet?*' the girl went on.

'Then you'll get dirty wet feet!' the boy replies.

And he jumps right in to the nearest puddle. Because what's more important at that moment is the sheer enjoyment and excitement of splashing in puddles.

And so that's what they do all morning - laugh and jump and splash.

And do you know? The next day all the puddles have gone and the girl realises that the opportunity has gone too. But she's glad to have enjoyed it when she did. For who knows when it will rain so much again?

Therapeutic goals:

- Confidence/self-belief

SUIT OF ARMOUR
(for boys)

You may agree with me that it's fun to pick clothes out of the dressing up box and play being someone else for a moment, like a superhero or a witch or wizard, or maybe even a ghost. But one boy did not like to dress up. He was happy, had lots of friends and liked to do lots of other things and his teacher was puzzled by this.

'Why don't you want to play with the dressing up clothes?' The teacher asked the boy.

'Because I'm already wearing my suit of armour,' the boy replied.

His teacher laughed. *'But you're not wearing a suit of armour! Fancy saying that!'*

'I am,' the boy went on, *'I have it on over my clothes, that's why I don't need to dress up.'*

The teacher decided to play along with the boy and said: *'So, tell me, why are you wearing a suit of armour?'*

'Because it helps me be happy,' the boy said. *'No matter what happens, it protects me. If people say things I don't like, it turns their words into an arrow, which pings against my armour and falls to the ground.'*

And the teacher realised that even though it was invisible, the boy's suit of armour was just as real as all the clothes in the dressing up box. In fact, because it made him strong, the suit of armour would last longer than the superhero, witch, wizard or ghost clothes.

And as the boy walked away, his teacher just thought she could see that suit of armour glint in the sun.

Therapeutic goals:
- Confidence/self belief
- Overcoming bullying

SUIT OF ARMOUR
(for girls)

You may agree with me that it's fun to pick clothes out of the dressing up box and play being someone else for a moment, like a superhero or a witch or wizard or maybe even a ghost. But one girl did not like to dress up. She was happy and had lots of friends and liked to do lots of other things and her teacher was puzzled by this.

'Why don't you want to play with the dressing up clothes?' The teacher asked the girl.

'Because I'm already wearing my suit of armour,' the girl said.

Her teacher laughed. *'But you're not wearing a suit of armour! Fancy saying that!'*

'I am,' the girl went on. *'I have it on over my clothes, that's why I don't need to dress up.'*

The teacher decided to play along with the girl and said: *'So, tell me, why are you wearing a suit of armour?'*

'Because it helps me be happy,' the girl said. *'No matter what happens, it protects me. If people say things I don't like, it turns their words into an arrow, which pings against my armour and falls to the ground.'*

And the teacher knew that even though it was invisible, the girl's suit of armour was just as real as all the clothes in the dressing up box. In fact, because it made her strong, the suit of armour would last longer than the superhero, witch, wizard or ghost clothes.

And as the girl skipped away, her teacher just thought she could see that suit of armour glint in the sun.

Therapeutic goals:
- Confidence/self-belief
- Overcoming bullying

TABBY CAT
(for boys)

As you may know, cats love to go out at night. They have eyes which can see in the dark. They have whiskers on the sides and tops of the heads, which means they can feel where they are. They can also jump up and down great heights.

In one town, there was a street where all the cats lived in different houses. Each night, their families would shut them out and they would meet. One cat was tabby, one was black, one was white and one was grey. They were not like each other at all. And just as each cat was different, so they wanted to do different things.

The tabby cat wanted to make sure nights were arranged his way. *'We will walk over the tiles to the field and then catch mice together tonight,'* he said.

The others yawned and stretched. *'I don't think so,'* they said. *'We did that yesterday. It would be nice to do something else tonight.'*

'Why?' said the tabby, annoyed. *'We enjoyed it last time!'*

The other cats moved away from him a little because he seemed cross with them and because he wasn't listening.

The more the tabby told the other cats what to do, the less interested they became. Soon after, they walked away from him looking over their shoulders at him.

'*Suit yourself!*' he called after them.

And the tabby went on his own to hunt for mice. It was lonely. It would be so much more fun with the other cats. He wondered why he was alone. His idea had been good, hadn't it?

And then he remembered the faces of the other cats, as they looked over their shoulders at him as they walked away. He remembered how the more he told them what to do, the less interested they were. And he knew that he hadn't listened at all. And this was why he was alone.

He licked his shoulder (because that is what cats do when they are embarrassed) and the tabby cat vowed not to spend a night hunting alone again.

And do you know, that tabby cat never directly told the other cats what to do from that night on because he had learned a lesson. And by listening to the ideas of the other cats he learnt about many more places to play and hunt because everyone had a turn.

Therapeutic goals:
- Making friends/developing social skills

TABBY CAT
(for girls)

As you may know, cats love to go out at night. They have eyes which can see in the dark. They have whiskers on the sides and tops of the heads, which means they can feel where they are. They can also jump up and down great heights.

In one town, there was a street where all the cats lived in different houses. Each night, their families would shut them out and they would meet. One cat was tabby, one was black, one was white and one was grey. They were not like each other at all. And just as each cat was different, so they wanted to do different things.

The tabby cat wanted to make sure nights were arranged her way. '*We will walk over the tiles to the field and then catch mice together tonight,*' she said.

The others yawned and stretched. '*I don't think so,*' they said. '*We did that yesterday. It would be nice to do something else tonight.*'

'*Why?*' said the tabby, annoyed. '*We enjoyed it last time!*'

The other cats moved away from her a little because she seemed cross with them and because she wasn't listening.

The more the tabby told the other cats what to do, the less interested they became. Soon after, they walked away from her looking over their shoulders at her.

'*Suit yourself!*' she called after them.

And the tabby went on her own to hunt for mice. It was lonely. It would be so much more fun with the other cats. She wondered why she was alone. Her idea had been good, hadn't it?

And then she remembered the faces of the other cats, as they looked over their shoulders at her as they walked away. She remembered how the more she told them what to do, the less interested they were. And she knew that she hadn't listened at all. And this was why she was alone.

She licked her shoulder (because that is what cats do when they are embarrassed) and the tabby cat vowed not to spend a night hunting alone again.

And do you know, that tabby cat never directly told the other cats what to do from that night on because she had learned a lesson. And by listening to the ideas of the other cats she learnt about many more places to play and hunt because everyone had a turn.

Therapeutic goals:

- Making friends/developing social skills

TEDDY AND THE SPACESHIP

Now, in space, as you will know, there are many planets. Some are near to their suns and are hot and some are far away and are cold. Some planets are mostly made of gasses and some are mostly made of rock and dust. Some planets have oceans and some have ice. There is a lot of variety because the universe is a beautiful, precious and mysterious place. And, in the future, we will know much more about space than we do now.

For example, in the future, when a family moves house, they may not only move to another street, town or country but to another planet. Just imagine, flying in a spaceship to another world! How strange and exciting.

And this was what was happening to one particular family. And although everyone knew it had to happen, it did not make it easier for some of the toys in the toy box.

Teddy was the most upset because he loved the planet he and the family were on.

'*Why do we have to go?*' he asked. '*I like it here. I think this is the best planet in the universe.*'

And the Gorilla, who was a friend of Teddy, and had spent years in the toy box with him said: '*But if you have never been to the other planet before, how do you know that for sure?*'

And the Teddy thought for a moment and realised that it was true, he had never visited the new planet and so it was possible that it may be just as good as where he was. Or, in fact, it could even be better.

'*And,*' continued the Gorilla, '*you wouldn't want to be left behind would you?*'

The Teddy said quite decidedly: '*No, I don't want to be left behind.*' Teddy knew that it would be better to be with the family on the new planet than on his own on the old one.

And, so, not long after, the toy box (with the Teddy and the Gorilla safely inside), flew in a spaceship with the family to another planet.

And instead of just feeling sad to leave, a part of Teddy secretly felt excited too.

Therapeutic goals:
- Accepting change
- Moving house

THE ELEMENTS

There are five elements: Earth, Water, Wind, Air and Fire.

The element of Earth said to the others: '*Everything needs soil to grow, there would be no woods, crops or plants without me.*'

The element of Fire felt sad that it couldn't make things grow because all it could do was make things hot and burnt.

The element of Water said: '*Well, everyone needs water to drink and there would be no rain, rivers and seas without me. I am definitely the most important element.*'

The element of Fire felt sad that it couldn't stop people feeling thirsty, in fact all it could do was make things hot and burnt.

The element of Wind said: '*Well, everyone needs wind, boats would not sail, wind turbines would not turn and the world would be stagnant without me. I am definitely the most important element.*'

The element of Fire felt sad that it couldn't help sail a boat, in fact all it could do was make things hot and burnt.

The element of Air said: '*Well, everyone needs air. I allow every living creature to breathe, without me there would be no people or animals alive. I am definitely the most important element.*'

And the element of Fire felt sad because it couldn't help people breathe, in fact all it could do was make things hot and burnt.

But, that Winter, a cold spell came over the world. The earth frosted, the water froze, the wind stopped and the air chilled. Everything was very, very cold and what was needed was warmth.

And all over the world, fires were lit to keep the people and animals warm. They needed Fire to stay alive. They needed Fire as much as they needed any other element and at that moment, they needed it the most.

And the element of Fire quietly warmed everyone and Fire glowed with the knowledge that it was every bit as valuable as the other four elements.

The elements of Earth, Water, Wind and Air did not brag about themselves again because they knew how important Fire was, but in a completely different way.

Therapeutic goals:
- Accepting yourself for who you are
- Confidence/self-belief

TREASURE HUNT
(for boys)

Going on a treasure hunt can be a lot of fun. Answering clues and moving closer and closer to the treasure is exciting. One boy loved it. He wasn't sure what the treasure would be, but he knew that he wanted it all to himself. After all, if he was clever enough to answer all the clues first, he felt he deserved to have all the prize!

And because he was a clever boy, he did answer all the clues. And he was the first of all the children to find the treasure box.

The box was wooden and smooth to touch. There was a brass latch, which he opened. And inside the treasure box was chocolate of many different kinds. And the boy grinned in delight - it was all his!

Just then, all the other children crowded round him - they had caught up with him and wanted to see what was inside the box.

He said: *'This is my treasure. I found it first!'*

The children frowned at him.

He looked at their faces and felt a distance growing between himself and them. He knew that if he took the treasure box for himself and bragged about it again, that distance would stay there long after the treasure hunt was over.

And so the boy said: '*Please have some chocolate everyone.*'

And the children smiled at him because they could see that he was the sort of person who liked to share, and they liked him for that. And each child took chocolate from the treasure box.

But the truth was, he received a bigger gift through his generosity, which was their friendship.

Therapeutic goals:
- Making friends/developing social skills

TREASURE HUNT
(for girls)

Going on a treasure hunt can be a lot of fun. Answering clues and moving closer and closer to the treasure is exciting. One girl loved it. She wasn't sure what the treasure would be, but she knew that she wanted it all to herself. After all, if she was clever enough to answer all the clues first, she felt she deserved to have all the prize!

And because she was a clever girl, she did answer all the clues. And she was the first of all the children to find the treasure box.

The box was wooden and smooth to touch. There was a brass latch, which she opened. And inside the treasure box was chocolate of many different kinds. And the girl grinned in delight - it was all hers!

Just then, all the other children crowded round her - they had caught up with her and wanted to see what was inside the box.

She said: *'This is my treasure. I found it first!'*

The children frowned.

She looked at their faces and felt a distance growing between herself and them. She knew that if she took the treasure box for herself and bragged about it, that distance would stay there long after the treasure hunt was over.

And so the girl said: '*Please have some chocolate everyone.*'

And the children smiled at her because they could see that she was the sort of person who liked to share, and they liked her for that. And each child took chocolate from the treasure box.

But the truth was, she received a bigger gift through her generosity, which was their friendship.

Therapeutic goals:
- Making friends/developing social skills

UNCOMFORTABLE STONE

I wonder if you can think of a time when you have walked with a stone in your shoe. How annoying it is! There is no forgetting it's there of course, rubbing away. The first thing you want to do when you feel that stone, is to take off your shoe and shake out the stone.

And that's how you should be with anything that makes you feel upset and uncomfortable. Remember to take off your shoe and shake out the stone. Because, without that, you can be sure that the stone will keep rubbing you. But once this is done, you can walk, run, skip, dance, play, jump and climb. The world is there - ready for you!

Therapeutic goals:
- Emotional/sexual abuse
- Neglect
- Overcoming bullying
- Physical abuse

WHALE SONG
(for boys)

Let's imagine a beautiful, dark, blue ocean which goes on as far as the eye can see. And, there, popping up in the water, is the back of a young, grey whale, who some people call a calf. He lives with his mother and father and the other whales in what some people call a pod. It's a wonderful life for a calf, diving and swimming in the ocean. In the future, he will swim and hunt for fish in the cool sea, far to the south.

The trouble is, although he's quick and swims well, he can't sing whale song like the other whales of his age. He has no control of his voice and this makes him shy and embarrassed. Sometimes his notes are too high and sometimes they are too low and sometimes they don't come at all! The whale is ashamed and does not know what to do about it. He so wants to be good at singing.

He remembers how he learnt to swim and he knows that he has learnt to do that himself. He thinks about the way he dives and he knows that he has also learnt to do that himself.

And then he realises that he can control the way he sings because singing is no different. All he needs is belief that he can sing and the time and patience to try. And so the calf sings every day. Each time he tries, his notes became more and more tuneful, until one day, without really realising it, he is just as good at singing as all the other whales of his age.

And the problem is gone. Now, he can sing on the way to the cold ocean waters, with all the other whales.

Therapeutic goals:
- Confidence/self-belief
- Control of bladder and bowels
- Gaining independence

WHALE SONG
(for girls)

Let's imagine a beautiful, dark, blue ocean which goes on as far as the eye can see. And, there, popping up in the water, is the back of a young, grey whale, who some people call a calf. She lives with her mother and father and the other whales in what some people call a pod. It's a wonderful life for a calf, diving and swimming in the ocean. In the future, she will swim and hunt for fish in the cool sea, far to the south.

The trouble is, although she's quick and swims well, she can't sing whale song like the other whales of her age. She has no control of her voice and this makes her shy and embarrassed. Sometimes her notes are too high and sometimes they are too low and sometimes they don't come at all! The whale is ashamed and does not know what to do about it. She so wants to be good at singing.

She remembers how she learnt to swim and she knows that she has learnt to do that herself. She thinks about the way she dives and she knows that she has also learnt to do that herself.

And she then realises that she can control the way she sings because singing is no different. All she needs is belief that she can sing and the time and patience to try. And so, the calf sings every day. Each time she tries, her notes became more and more tuneful, until one day, without really realising it, she is just as good at singing as all the others.

And the problem is gone. Now, she can sing on the way to the cold ocean waters, with all the other whales.

Therapeutic goals:
- Confidence/self-belief
- Control of bladder and bowels
- Gaining independence

WINDS OF CHANGE
(for boys)

I wonder if you can picture a beautiful boat, with long, white sails and a large wooden deck. Maybe it's gliding through the cool, blue water with the sun glinting on the sails. And maybe there is a boy, like you perhaps, living on this boat with his family.

The boy loves its large, wooden deck. Every morning, he wakes and looks through the porthole and smiles when he sees the sea. The dolphins who live in the water make friendly clicking noises when they see him and jump and dive around the boat.

At night, the sky is very big and full of stars and he often looks up at it in wonder.

Then, one day, his parents tell him: *'We can't live in the boat any more, it's time to move.'*

The boy does not know how he will manage without the dolphins, his bedroom with the porthole and the big night sky. He asks: *'Can I stay on the boat?'*

'I'm sorry we can't,' they reply. *'We have to leave because we have important new things to do.'*

The boy realises that he is definitely going.

'I must be brave and try and be happy,' he says to himself.

His parents ask him to pack his things.

'I must be brave and try and be happy,' he says to himself again.

The family move to a very different home, on dry land. The boy is used to everything moving with the sway of the water but now everything is still. The family's new home is new and strange to him. They have a garden instead of the sea. And a house to live in, instead of a boat. And his bedroom has a square window instead of a porthole. And the boy looks at all these new things with curiosity.

He remembers the dolphins and the boat with the white sails.

'I must be brave and try and be happy,' he says to himself.

But time can make you think differently about things. And as the months pass, the house in its cosy lane, with its garden full of cheerful birds becomes more and more familiar to him.

And, best of all, he has neighbours - and it is fun for the boy to play with children next door. He will always hold the dolphins in his heart but, in time, the house truly becomes his home.

Therapeutic goals:
- Accepting change
- Developing resilience
- Gaining independence
- Moving house

WINDS OF CHANGE
(for girls)

I wonder if you can picture a beautiful boat, with long, white sails and a large wooden deck. Maybe it's gliding through the cool, blue water with the sun glinting on the sails. And maybe there is a girl, like you perhaps, living on this boat with her family.

The girl loves its large, wooden deck. Every morning, she wakes and looks through the porthole and smiles when she sees the sea. The dolphins who live in the water make friendly clicking noises when they see her and jump and dive around the boat.

At night, the sky is very big and full of stars and she often looks up at it in wonder.

Then, one day, her parents tell her: *'We can't live in the boat any more, it's time to move.'*

The girl does not know how she will manage without the dolphins, her bedroom with the porthole and the big night sky. She asks her parents: *'Can I stay on the boat?'*

'I'm sorry we can't,' they reply. *'We have to leave because we have important new things to do.'*

The girl realises that she is definitely going.

'I must be brave and try and be happy,' she says to herself.

Her parents ask her to pack her things.

'I must be brave and try and be happy,' she says to herself again.

The family move to a very different home, on dry land. The girl is used to everything moving with the sway of the water but now everything is still. The family's new home is new and strange to her. They have a garden instead of the sea. And a house to live in, instead of a boat. And her bedroom has a square window instead of a porthole. And the girl looks at all these new things with curiosity.

She remembers the dolphins and the boat with the white sails.

'I must be brave and try and be happy,' she says to herself.

But time can make you think differently about things. And as the months pass, the house in its cosy lane, with its garden full of cheerful birds becomes more and more familiar to her.

And, best of all, she has neighbours - and it is fun for the girl to play with children next door. She will always hold the dolphins in her heart but, in time, the house truly becomes her home.

Therapeutic goals:
- Accepting change
- Developing resilience
- Gaining independence
- Moving house

WORRYING WAVE
(for boys)

The seas are full of waves. And where the moon is in our sky tells the waves when to come in and out of the shore.

The one wave we are interested in, is nicknamed 'Worry.' He lives in a part of the world where there are long, white, sandy beaches and there is hot, sunny weather. He likes moving in and out of the beach, lapping up to the sand and retreating again. It feels safe.

But things never stay exactly the same and, one day, a storm whirls up. The sky goes dark. The wind begins to blow. The waves know they will pound up that long, sandy beach - rather than lap against the sand.

And 'Worry' cries out: *'We may bring jellyfish up on the sand!'*

'Yes,' the other waves reply, *'we may.'*

'Worry' cries out again: *'We may hurt ourselves against the shore!'*

'*Waves will crash sometimes,*' the other waves reply.

'Worry' cries out again: '*We may get moved to another place after the storm! We may even end up in another part of the ocean!*'

'*We may,*' the other waves reply, '*but that could be an adventure. Have courage Worry.*'

And 'Worry' feels the momentum of the wind and the storm and the other waves. And he hears them cheer and laugh. He knows that they are excited that the storm is coming. Secretly, 'Worry' wants to have fun too. And so, in that moment, he decides to give himself up to the storm.

He and the other waves crash against the white sandy beach and although it is new, it is also great fun. 'Worry' even laughs with all the other waves. He notices that the beach is covered in people in wetsuits and on surf boards. They are delighted too because the waves are the best kind to surf in.

The next day, when the storm is over and the sun comes out, our wave goes up and back on the sand he's so familiar with. And no one ever thinks to call him

'Worry' again because after the storm he knows that he has no need to be frightened.

Therapeutic goals:
- Confidence/self-belief

WORRYING WAVE
(for girls)

The seas are full of waves. And where the moon is in our sky tells the waves when to come in and out of the shore.

The one wave we are interested in is nicknamed 'Worry.' She lives in a part of the world where there are long, white, sandy beaches and there is hot, sunny weather. She likes moving in and out of the beach, lapping up to the sand and retreating again. It feels safe.

But things never stay exactly the same and, one day, a storm whirls up. The sky goes dark. The wind begins to blow. The waves know they will pound up that long, sandy beach - rather than lap against the sand.

And 'Worry' cries out: '*We may bring jellyfish up on the sand!*'

'*Yes,*' the other waves reply, '*we may.*'

'Worry' cries out again: '*We may hurt ourselves against the shore!*'

'*Waves will crash sometimes,*' the other waves reply.

'Worry' cries out again: '*We may get moved to another place after the storm! We may even end up in another part of the ocean!*'

'*We may,*' the other waves reply, '*but that could be an adventure. Have courage Worry.*'

And 'Worry' feels the momentum of the wind and the storm and the other waves. And she hears them cheer and laugh. She knows that they are excited that the storm is coming.

Secretly, 'Worry' wants to have fun too. And so, in that moment, she decides to give herself up to the storm.

She and the other waves crash against the white sandy beach and although it is new, it's also great fun.

'Worry' even laughs with all the other waves. She notices that the beach is covered in people in wetsuits and on surf boards. They are delighted too because the waves are the best kind to surf in.

The next day, when the storm is over and the sun comes out, our wave goes up and back on the sand she's so familiar with. And no one ever thinks to call her 'Worry' again because after the storm she knows that she has no need to be frightened.

Therapeutic goals:
- Confidence/self-belief

BIBLIOGRAPHY

Aesop (2016) *Aesop's Fables: Complete Collection* CreateSpace Independent Publishing Platform

Hudson L (2009) *Scripts and Strategies in Hypnotherapy with Children,* Crowne House Publishing Ltd

Owen N (2001) *The Magic of Metaphor: 77 Stories for Teachers, Trainers and Thinkers,* Crowne House Publishing Ltd.

Rosen S (1982) *My Voice Will Go With You: The Teaching Tales of Milton H Erikson,* WW Norton and Company Inc

Taschen (2010) *The Book of Symbols: Reflections on Archetypal Images* The Archive for Research in Archetypal Symbolism